Dragons Need Sleep

WRITTEN AND ILLUSTRATED BY
PILAR MARIE

DEDICATION

This book is dedicated to my parents, Fred and Lili. Without their love and support, this book would never have been published.

Everyone screamed when they saw Fryer—
a terrible dragon the color of fire!

He soared in the sky before he swooped down,
scaring the people in villages and towns.

He came to a stop and stomped all around,
knocking down trees and shaking the ground.

His breath sizzled fire, his nostrils blew smoke,
and he burned the land whenever he spoke:

He snarled to show teeth as sharp as knives,
and all ran away, afraid for their lives!

He spent every day this exact same way—
chasing the people far, far away.

Then he quietly flew on home
to a cave in a hill where he lived, all alone.

There he ate waffles of every type

and played for hours by firelight.

But when it got late and he started to snore,

he'd wake right back up, feeling cranky and sore.

Maybe the ground was hard...

The light

was bright...

Or he had too much fun,
playing all night...

But he never got rest, week after week,
and felt meaner the longer he went without sleep.

So, each morning, off he would fly
to attack more towns and villages nearby.

Until, one day, things changed for Fryer, as he raged around, breathing fire.

As he stomped about and he huffed and puffed, some kids in town thought enough was enough.

They carefully went up to the dragon, pulling a doll in a little toy wagon.

"Fryer," they said. "You need to stop that.
We're awfully tired. It's time for our nap.

We can't rest when you're knocking down trees,
shaking the ground, and causing these screams."

"Please find something quiet to do,
at least for the next hour or two."

Then they knowingly looked at the dragon, and pulled something up out of their wagon.

"Here," they said. "Take our blankie. You should nap too. Then you won't be so cranky."

The others in town gasped in shock,

as Fryer the Fierce stopped and he thought...

...and he thought...

Then he reached for the blanket,
soft and warm, lovingly used,
edges tattered and torn.

"Thank you," he whispered and
started to cry, giant tears
falling down from each eye.

"Oh, Fryer," the children all sighed.
"We know you're not mean, you're just over-tired!"

"It's true!" Fryer sobbed, "I don't take naps."

"I don't sleep at night. I just can't relax!"

"We'll help!" the kids said, "It's easy. You'll see.
Come and lie down in the shade of these trees.

To sleep you need to find the right spot —
One that's dark and quiet and soft."

"Then find something like a toy
that makes you feel safe or that brings you joy."

Fryer lay down under the trees,
holding the blankie in the cool spring breeze.

But it didn't work, he couldn't sleep,
and Fryer the Fierce continued to weep.

"Fryer," a boy said, "I'm not surprised.
To fall asleep, you must close your eyes!"

Fryer closed first his left then right eye,
but stayed wide awake and sadly sighed.

"Oh, silly us, we forgot one thing!
Sometimes, to sleep, you need someone to sing!"

The kids all sang a nice, sweet song,
and Fryer's tears were completely gone.

Then Fryer smiled the biggest smile
and felt happier than he had felt in awhile.

And that was it. He began to snore,
each snore louder than the one before.

For several days and nights he rested,
and when he woke up, he felt refreshed.

Then, as he sat in the shade of the trees,
Fryer was calm and filled with peace.

He was no longer mean, or angry, or crabby,
but now he was nice, and joyful, and happy.

He started to spend time planting trees,
building homes, and sharing waffle recipes.

He now has friends who are like family—
he's never alone and rarely unhappy.

His new favorite thing is to play with the kids,
and as they play tag, he says as he grins:

"I'm Fryer the Fierce. Fear me!
Or I'll give you the biggest hug ever seen!"

But he saves the
snuggliest snuggle
of all...

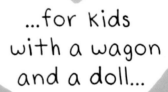

...for kids
with a wagon
and a doll...

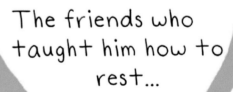

The friends who
taught him how to
rest...

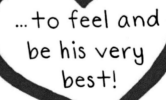

...to feel and
be his very
best!

THE END

THANK YOU FOR YOUR SUPPORT

Thank you for reading Dragons Need Sleep. If you enjoyed it, please consider leaving a review. I appreciate each and every comment.

ABOUT THE AUTHOR

Pilar Marie is an army wife and a mother to four young children. She has bachelor's degrees in English and science and a master's in elementary education.

She can be reached at pilarmariebooks@gmail.com with any questions or special requests.

18604243R00021

Hawaiʻi Sun
Aloha Moon

Bryant,
It was a pleasure meeting you.
Good luck on the mainland. Make sure
you bring some Aloha with you.
Take care,
Brownlee

Bryant,
Take it easy Homie.
May God bless you
in your every endeavor!
SFC Miller

BRYANT
HOPE YOU ENJOYED
@ DISA-PAC. GOOD
FUTURE ENDEAVORS
PE13.

Bryant,
Fair winds & following seas.
Take care of you & yours.
YN(SW) Savin

BRYANT,
It's been nice
knowing you - Hopefully
you enjoyed it here with us.
ODIE

BRYANT~
THANKS FOR ALL
YOUR HELP INPUTTING
ALL THE TRAINING. YOU
TOOK A BIG LOAD OFF MY
SHOULDERS. HOPE YOU
ENJOYED YOUR STAY AT
DISA-PAC. I'M GLAD YOU
GOT TO DO SOME FUN THINGS
WHILE YOU WERE HERE &
HOPE YOU GET TO COME
BACK.
ALOHA-
DONNA

Bryant,
Was great having
you here. Don't forget
us when you go back to
the "Real" world.
CDR Kerr

Bryant,
Thanks for
making DISA-PAC
a true 'OHANA!
You will be missed
Take care and good
luck!
CDR Dean

Bryant,
Thanks for being a
part of our team!
You've been a
valuable asset
and a great friend
Take care as you
progress to a
higher level!
-Todd

Bryant-
Hope you enjoyed your brief
stint in paradise and that
it was a worthwhile an experience
for you as having you here was
for us.
May the heavens
rain wisdom on you
and lift you above all.
Aloha
Bernie Takano
TR

Bryant,
It was a pleasure knowing.
I wish you the best as you
move on to bigger and better
things. Most of all, thanks for
caring when I was ill.
God Bless, Jerome (Chief B)

"All the time our visits to the islands have been more like dreams than realities: the people, the life, the beachcombers, the old stories and songs…so interesting; the climate, the scenery, … so beautiful."

ROBERT LOUIS STEVENSON (1889)

Front cover: March sunset at Puʻuhonua o Hōnaunau, Hawaiʻi. *Back cover:* Moonrise framed by the Mokulua isles, Lanikai, Oʻahu *Title page:* September moonset over Niʻihau at sunrise frōm Waimea Canyon Road, Kauaʻi. *This page:* June moonrise over the Na Pali Coast, Kauaʻi. *Opposite page:* January sunset with sailboat, Waikīkī Beach, Oʻahu.

Hawai'i Sun Aloha Moon

A Collection of Photography
by James Rigler and Gail Ward

ISLAND HERITAGE

Dedication

*This book is dedicated to those who love
the islands of Hawai'i and the spirit of aloha.*

January sunset, Sans Souci Beach, O'ahu.

March moonrise (blue moon) over the lava flow of Puʻu ʻŌʻō Vent, Hawaiʻi.

March moonset at dawn near Kūhiō Beach with outrigger canoe and surfboards, Oʻahu.

Moonchasing

Like so many before us we had a reason to travel to this small group of islands out in the middle of the Pacific Ocean, the most remote place on the planet. We came to chase the full moon and capture it on film. The moon led us… the Hawaiʻi sun pursued us, enticing us to turn around and photograph its grandeur. After all, that fiery red ball gives the moon its brilliance. What we discovered in our quest of lā and mahina "the sun and moon" was the aloha spirit, undiminished by time, warm and friendly, living in this rugged, beautiful and distant paradise.

Early travelers to these islands, explorers on horseback, wrote of the flowers, ocean, moonlight, volcanic eruptions, huge waves, sunsets, wonderful fruit, and Hawaiian traditions. More than 100 years later and just before the millennium we traveled to these islands with the same desire for discovery and adventure. Airplanes have replaced the steamships and four-wheel drive vehicles have replaced the horse. We used a camera instead of a journal to record our observations. We learned, as they did in that earlier time, about the real Hawaiʻi — the history, the land, and the people. We left, as they did, with the spirit of aloha.

Hoʻomākaʻikaʻi translates as "to take on a visit." This collection of photographs is our way of taking you on a visit to the islands as we found them.

March sunset near the cottage where King Kalākaua once lived, Keauhou, Hawaiʻi.

May moonrise at Hāna, Maui.

"I came to a grove of tall coconut trees ...reaching straight up sixty or seventy feet and topped with a spray of green foliage sheltering clusters of coconuts — not more picturesque than a forest of colossal ragged parasols, with bunches of magnified grapes under them..."

MARK TWAIN (1866)

Opposite left: Moonrise with palm trees at Kaʻalāwai Beach, Oʻahu. *Opposite right:* Moonrise toward Koko Head from Kaʻalāwai Beach, Oʻahu. *Above:* Moonrise over Hāna Harbor, Maui. *Right:* Moonrise beyond the Spouting Horn, Kauaʻi.

Color and Light

We came to the islands to photograph their beauty during the hours from dusk through dawn, when the light is low, soft and enchanting. None of these images has been enhanced with filters or manipulated by computers. What you see is a result of the natural occurrence of sunlight and moonlight filtered through the tropical air, creating its impression on film. Apart from dealing with the forces of wind and rain, our biggest challenge was to be in the right place at the right time.

March moonset just before dawn on Waikīkī Beach, O'ahu.

January moonrise just after sunset from Lanikai Beach toward Moku Nui, Oʻahu.

Hoʻihi "to treat with respect"

In paying our respect to traditional Hawaiian heritage and culture we sought out historic and sacred sites, from the navigational stones to the birthplace of Kamehameha I — Kamehameha the Great, often known as "The Lonely One" — who was the first aliʻi, "chief or ruler" to unite all of the Hawaiian Islands.

Opposite left: March sunset at navigational stones, Hawaiʻi. *Opposite right:* March moonrise over Kamehameha Ahuʻena Heiau, the birthplace of Kamehameha the Great, Hawaiʻi. *Left:* April moonrise over Moʻokini Heiau, Hawaiʻi. *Right top:* April sunset, Moʻokini Heiau, Hawaiʻi.
Right bottom: Detail of the Piʻilanihale Heiau, perhaps the largest construction project in ancient Hawaiʻi, located in Kahanu Garden, Hāna, Maui.

Easter morning April moonrise in the Waipiʻo Valley where Kamehameha the Great was raised and taught the ancient ways, Hawaiʻi.

July moonrise toward Pololū Valley where it is said the stones were carried hand over hand to build the Moʻokini Heiau and Puʻukoholā Heiau, Hawaiʻi.

July moonrise over Puʻukoholā "Hill of the Whale" Heiau, built in 1790-1791 by Kamehameha the Great to the war god Kū, to gain the god's help in conquering the Islands and bringing peace to his people. Mauna Kea can be seen in the background, Hawaiʻi.

April moonrise over 500-year-old Lapakahi Village where crops were planted under the proper phase of the moon, Hawai'i.

Above: April moonrise over a palm tree in Lapakahi Village, Hawai'i. *Top right:* April sunset through the Hala Trees in Lapakahi Village, Hawai'i. *Bottom right:* October moonrise at the Royal Coconut Grove in Kapuāiwa, Moloka'i.

Hala and Lā'au Niu "pandanus and coconut trees"

Pandanus and coconut trees provided staples for the early Hawaiians. The Islanders had many uses for parts of these trees, such as medicine, body oils, food, love charm, 'ūkēkē "striking musical bows," lei, paint brushes, mats, canoe sails, baskets, utensils, drums, fans, pillows, kites, sandals, house posts, house roofs and sides, nets, cords and fuels.

May sunrise on the Alakoko Fishpond, Kaua'i.

Loko i'a "fishpond"

Fishponds were built on the coasts where waters were shallow and flat. They were tended by the maka'āinana "common people" for the ali'i "royalty". Small fish were free to go in and out but larger fish were trapped to maintain a constant supply. The island of Moloka'i is known for its fishponds. The legend of the Alakoko Fishpond on the island of Kaua'i is that it was built in a single night as a gift for a prince and princess by the menehune — a mythical people much like the beloved leprechauns of Ireland — who worked only at night by the light of the moon. There are many fishponds, some are still in use along the coastlines of the islands.

February moonrise over the Aliʻi Fishpond, Molokaʻi.

June moonset on the Alakoko Fishpond, Kauaʻi.

April moonset across the fishpond at ʻAnaehoʻomalu Beach, Hawaiʻi.

Left: November moonrise from Puʻu Pehe, Lānaʻi toward Haleakalā, Maui. *Above:* May sunset behind Molokini Crater from ʻĀhihi Bay, Maui. *Below:* Heliconia. *Opposite page:* December moonrise at Mokoliʻi Island, Oʻahu.

Top: August moonset at dawn from Puʻuhonua o Hōnaunau, Hawaiʻi. *Bottom:* Reflections at dawn in the tide pools at Puʻuhonua o Hōnaunau, Hawaiʻi.

"There are times and places where the past becomes more vivid than the present, and memory dominates the ear and eye. I have found it so in the presence of the vestiges of Rome; I have found it so again in the [Place] of Refuge at Hōnaunau…"

ROBERT LOUIS STEVENSON (1889)

August moonset at dawn from Puʻuhonua o Hōnaunau, Hawaiʻi.

This Place of Refuge at Hōnaunau on the Big Island is one of the most beautiful and peaceful places in the islands. It was, and is, a sanctuary. It is here that one can imagine what life in Hawaiʻi might have been before the arrival of Captain James Cook in 1778. The Hawaiians believed that lava flows, tidal waves, famine and earthquakes were punishment for offending the gods. In order to protect their way of life and that of the royalty, they created a rigid set of rules and kapu "laws." A kapu-breaker was pursued until caught and killed. But if the kapu-breaker could reach a puʻuhonua, a kahuna "priest" would perform a ceremony of absolution and the offender could go free. Defeated warriors and non-combatants could also find refuge here during time of battle. The grounds outside the wall at Puʻuhonua o Hōnaunau were home to several generations of powerful chiefs.

Left: Kiʻi at Hale o Keawe, Puʻuhonua o Hōnaunau, Hawaiʻi. *Above:* Moonset over Kiʻi at Hale o Keawe. *Opposite page:* Moonset with canoe house at dawn at Puʻuhonua o Hōnaunau.

Left: March moonset at Hale o Keawe. *Right:* March moonset over Lono Kiʻi. Lono was the ancient Hawaiian god responsible for land fertility, Puʻuhonua o Hōnaunau. *Opposite page:* March sunset from Puʻuhonua o Hōnaunau, Hawaiʻi.

Opposite: August moonset of Kuʻemanu Heiau from Aliʻi Drive, Kailua-Kona, Hawaiʻi. *Above:* August moonset above St. Peter's Catholic Church (locally known as the Little Blue Church) near Kuʻemanu Heiau Aliʻi Drive, Hawaiʻi. *Right:* March sunset at lele hoʻokau "altar" of Kuʻemanu Heiau, surfing place of worship, Aliʻi Drive, Hawaiʻi.

Opposite top: March moonset at sunrise over the lava tube of Pu'u 'Ō'ō Vent. *Opposite bottom:* March moonset at sunrise over lava flowing into the ocean from Pu'u 'Ō'ō Vent.
Above: March moonset at sunrise over Pu'u 'Ō'ō Vent with the gentle slopes of Mauna Loa rising to heights of 13,677 feet in the distance.

To truly understand the natural forces of this island chain you need to experience the birthing of land on the southeastern side of the Big Island of Hawai'i. The 132 islands, reefs and shoals that make up the State of Hawai'i began in volcanic activity and grew from ocean depths to great heights. The eight main high islands are Hawai'i, Maui, O'ahu, Kaua'i, Moloka'i, Lāna'i, Ni'ihau and Kaho'olawe.

Within eyesight of Mauna Loa "long mountain," the earth's most massive volcano, the Pu'u 'Ō'ō vent on the flank of Kīlauea volcano is erupting. It pumps out an average of 400,000 cubic meters of lava per day which flows most of the time through a lava tube seven miles down to the ocean. Exceeding 2000°F, lava continuously pours over newly-created shoreline into the water where it sizzles and sends up an enormous steam cloud. Beyond this shore and due south about 30 kilometers is the still submerged, newly-forming island of Lō'ihi.

Above: Moonrise as we walked out over the 1992 lava flows.
Opposite page: Moonrise over the ocean as we approached the current lava flow.

Left: Moonrise capturing the image of Pele in the steam cloud. *Above:* James Rigler at lava's edge. *Opposite left:* Anthuriums near Volcano National Park, Hawai'i. *Opposite right:* Moonrise with fireworks from Madam Pele.

Pele is also the name given to the fire goddess of Hawai'i. If you are fortunate she may reveal her image in the glowing red steam clouds that can be seen at night near the water's edge. It is a difficult hike across a few miles of hardened lava. The terrain is uneven and the lava rock can cut like glass if you stumble. Most of the lava is pāhoehoe, which looks like swirls of chocolate fudge and creates a good surface for walking. The chunky lava a'ā, should be avoided. The best time to make this hike is at night in the moonlight, for in the daylight the heat can be unbearable. It is thrilling to be up close and to observe new land forming from the molten depths of the earth's core. Respect for the mana "power" of Pele is essential. Some observers who ventured too near have lost their lives.

Volcanic activity ended on Kaua'i's northwestern coast more than five million years ago. At that time the island looked dome-shaped with sloping sides, like Mauna Loa volcano on The Big Island of Hawai'i. Erosion from pounding winter surf and torrential rain carved away Kaua'i's original shield exposing the lava layers and other geologic features. This process continues today to carve changes in this beautiful and rugged stretch of coast.

Opposite: May moonrise at sunset over Mauna Pulu'ō Peak, Nā Pali Coast. *Top:* May moonrise at sunset along the Nā Pali Coast. *Bottom:* May moonrise at sunset Kalalau Valley, Nā Pali Coast. *Right:* Honopū sea arch, Nā Pali Coast.

Above: June moonrise over the Nā Pali Coast, Kauaʻi. *Top right:* September moonrise over lithified sand dunes of Māhāʻulepū, Kauaʻi. *Bottom right:* September
moonrise at sunset from Kawailoa Bay, Kauaʻi.

Left: February sunset north coastline cliffs with waterfall, Moloka'i. *Above:* February moonrise over Kalaupapa Peninsula, Moloka'i.

"Moloka'i ... along all its northern side plunges a front of precipice into a sea of unusual profundity. This range of cliff is, from east to west, the true end and frontier of the island. Only in one spot there projects to the ocean a certain triangular and rugged down, grassy, stony, windy ..."

ROBERT LOUIS STEVENSON (1890)

Opposite: Sunset from Hanalei Bay toward Mākena Peak, Kauaʻi. *Above left:* Sunrise over Kīlauea Lighthouse from Kalihiwai Road, Kauaʻi. *Above right:* Moonrise over a WWII Liberty Ship resting on the shallow reef at Shipwreck Beach, Lānaʻi.

June sunset through the Royal Coconut Grove toward Nounou Mountain, also called "The Sleeping Giant," Kaua'i.

May moonset toward Kalalea Mountain. This prominent peak is sometimes referred to as King Kong's Profile, Kaua'i.

September moonset with dog, Hanalei Bay, Kaua'i.

"It was a perfect morning. The full moon hung over the enclosing 'palis', gleaming on coffee and breadfruit groves, and on the surface of the river ..."

ISABELLA L. BIRD (1873)

Left: Moonrise over pineapple fields, Maui. *Above:* Coffee tree with ripe coffee cherries, Kona, Hawai'i. *Bottom left:* Moonset with papaya tree from Hono a Pi'ilani Highway toward the West Maui Mountains, Maui. *Bottom right:* Moonset over papaya plantation, Maui. *Below:* Mombo's Fruit Stand, Kaua'i. *Opposite:* Moonset over kalo (taro) fields on the Hanalei River, Kaua'i. Poi is made from the taro root.

"You must have fruit. You feel feel the want of it here."
MARK TWAIN (1866)

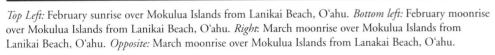
Top Left: February sunrise over Mokulua Islands from Lanikai Beach, O'ahu. *Bottom left:* February moonrise over Mokulua Islands from Lanikai Beach, O'ahu. *Right:* March moonrise over Mokulua Islands from Lanikai Beach, O'ahu. *Opposite:* March moonrise over Mokulua Islands from Lanakai Beach, O'ahu.

Niʻihau

For more than a century the privately-owned Niʻihau, oldest of the eight high islands, has been forbidden to outsiders to preserve the Hawaiian lifestyle of the less than 300 residents. The Hawaiian language is the first language of the Niʻihau people. Their culture and traditions are closely linked with Tahiti as expressed in mele "song" and hula "dance." The entire community is considered ʻohana "family." The island is mostly known for pūpū o Niʻihau, dove-type shells a half inch long which are found on the beaches and made into lei.

Opposite top: September moonset at dawn over the main island of Niʻihau. *Opposite bottom:* September moonset at dawn over Niʻihau and the Island of Lehua. *Left:* Princess plant. *Above:* September moonset at dawn over the low mountain and Kiʻi Landing.

The early Hawaiians cultivated sugar cane for food and sweetener. During the nineteenth and twentieth centuries sugar cane was grown extensively throughout the islands. Some sugar plantations and processing mills are still in operation on Kaua'i and Maui.

Opposite: Moonset over Ni'ihau at sunrise from a partially burnt cane field on Waimea Canyon Road, Kaua'i. *Left top:* Moonrise over cane fields toward the last crater to be formed on Kaua'i. *Left bottom:* Burning cane field along Waimea Canyon Road, Kaua'i. *Above:* Rainbow over sugar cane field of the West Maui Mountains, Maui.

Left top: Moonrise over the Hā'upu Range Tunnel Road, Kaua'i. *Left middle:* Moonrise from the cane fields over Old Kōloa Town the first sugar plantation town in the Islands, Kaua'i. *Left bottom:* Moonrise over cemetery on Kōloa Road, Kaua'i. *Above:* Moonrise over the Kōloa Sugar Mill (still operating), Kaua'i.

Moonrise over cane fields and Kōloa Sugar Mill from Weliweli Road, Kaua'i.

Opposite: February moonrise from ferry over Lahaina "Merciless Sun" and West Maui Mountains with rainbow's end on Maui's first volcano. *Left:* Sunset from Lahaina Harbor with the Carthaginian II, a two-masted schooner, toward the island of Lāna'i. *Right:* Sunset from Pioneer Inn, Lahaina, Maui looking toward the island of Lāna'i. Lahaina was not only a favorite spot for Hawaiian royality but also a whaling town in the 1800s.

Left: Sunset rainbow, Maui's first volcano. Kaua'i. *Right:* February moonrise Lahaina Harbor with the Carthaginian II and Pioneer Inn, Maui.

Left: Moonrise over Lahaina Harbor with West Maui Mountains. *Right:* Moonrise over West Maui Mountains with cruise ship.

Opposite: Moonset from the 'Īao Valley, Maui. *Above:* Moonset over the West Maui Mountains from the 'Īao "supreme light" Valley, Maui. *Far right:* Moonset at sunrise with Morning Glory and cactus over Kula cattle pasture, Maui. *Right:* King Protea grown in upcountry Maui.

Top: Moonrise from Haleakalā Crater with Mauna Kea in the far right background. *Left:* Moonrise, silversword on Red Hill, Haleakalā, Maui. *Middle:* Moonrise on Haleakalā toward Puʻu ʻUlaʻula overlook, Maui. *Right:* A moonchaser at the summit of Haleakalā. *Opposite left top:* Moonrise, silversword that bloomed and died on the summit. *Opposite left bottom:* Early morning moonset in the fog with Science City, satellite tracking station (University of Hawaiʻi). *Opposite right:* Moonset from the slopes of Haleakalā, Piʻilani Hwy. over Kalulu Crater with Island of Kahoʻolawe behind.

Haleakalā "House of the Sun"

Home to the nēnē "Hawaiian goose," and the ʻāhinahina "gray gray" silversword, this dormant volcano rises to 10,023 feet at Puʻu ʻUlaʻula peak. Whether at sunrise or moonrise, sunset or moonset, there is no view more beautiful than this one. From Haleakalā the demi-god Maui lassoed the sun to slow its passage and provide longer daylight, but even in daylight it can sometimes be cold, icy and foggy at the summit. The 360 degree panoramic view can be spectacular and can include the islands of Hawaiʻi, Lānaʻi, Molokaʻi, Oʻahu, Kahoʻolawe.

Opposite: Moonrise over Haleakalā with Molokini Crater. *This page left:* Moonrise from Lānaʻi Harbor with Haleakalā. *Top right:* Sunset at Hoʻokipa Park with wind surfer and surfers. A hazy Kahakuloa Head, Maui's Gibraltar, is in the distance. *Bottom right:* January sunrise over Diamond Head, Oʻahu.

July moonrise over Mauna Kea from Kohala, Hawai'i.

Mauna Kea "white mountain"

There is nothing quite like standing at 13,796 feet on the top of Mauna Kea with the sun setting and the full moon rising out of the clouds and over the shadow of the volcano. This sometimes snow-capped mountain is the home of the Hawai'i goddess of ice, Poli'ahu. Mauna Kea today is considered the premier astronomical observatory in the world. On the summit of this dormant (but not extinct) volcano there are observatories operated by several world powers.

Top: August moonrise over the shadow of Mauna Kea from the summit at sunset, Hawai'i.
Bottom: August moonrise over observatory at the summit of Mauna Kea, Hawai'i.

Above: Moonset over Hilo Bay with Mauna Kea to the right, Mauna Loa to the left, Hawai'i. *Right top:* Moonset over Coconut Island, Hilo Bay. The Hawaiians know this island as Mokuola, "healing island," and also as a pu'uhonua, "place of refuge." Mauna Kea and Mauna Loa can be seen in the distance. *Left bottom:* Wild orchid in fern forest outside of Hilo. *Right bottom:* Bridge at Lili'uokalani Gardens, Hilo.

Moonset just before dawn at Lili'uokalani Gardens, Hilo.

Above: Moonrise with cattle ranch near Hāwī, Hawai'i. *Top right:* Moonset over the Norfolk Pine of the little town of Maunaloa, Moloka'i. *Bottom right:* Moonset over Maunaloa once a pineapple company town, Moloka'i. *Opposite:* Moonrise over cactus with rainbow above Waimea ranchland, Hawai'i.

Left: May moonrise, Churches in Hāna, Maui. *Top right:* Moonrise over Hāna, Maui. *Bottom right:* Sunrise, St. Joseph Church Kaupō, Maui. *Opposite:* Moonset behind cattle ranch beyond Hāna near Lelekea Bay, Maui.

Top left: Moonrise, Lutheran Church Baldwin Avenue, Maui. *Top middle:* Moonrise, Holy Rosary Church with Damien Shrine, Baldwin Avenue, Maui. *Top right:* Moonrise, Lutheran Church Baldwin Avenue, Maui. *Left:* Moonrise, Mantokuji Buddhist Mission, Pā'ia, Maui.

Left: Moonrise from Lyon's Hill and the Paul I. Fagan memorial cross in Hāna. *Above:* Sunset toward Lyon's Hill and the Paul I. Fagan memorial cross in Hāna with volcanic craters of Haleakalā in the distance.

Opposite: Moonset over the "Little Blue Church" St. Peter's, from Ali'i Drive, Keauhou-Kona, Hawai'i. *Top:* Moonset over the Kona Theater, near Captain Cook, Hawai'i. *Bottom:* Coffee Plantation, Hawai'i. *Right:* Sunset with outrigger and cruise ship at Kailua-Kona, Hawai'i.

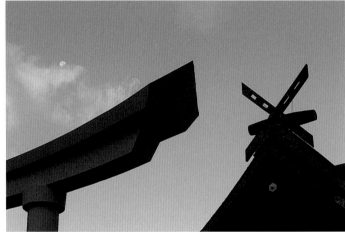

Top left: Moonset Honpa Hongwanji Hawai'i Betsuin Honolulu Temple, O'ahu. *Top right:* Moonset (detail) Kukui Health Building, O'ahu. *Bottom right:* Moonset Kukui Health Building, O'ahu. *Opposite:* Moonset at Byodo-In Temple toward Ko'olau Ridge, O'ahu.

Left: Moonset Lahaina Jodo Mission, Maui. *Top left and right:* Moonset, Soto Mission, Oʻahu.
Above: Moonset over St. Benedict's Painted Church, Hawaiʻi.

Top: Moonset upcountry on Lower Kula Road toward Holy Ghost Church on Easter Morning, Maui. *Bottom:* May moonset, cemetery in Kapa'a, Kaua'i. *Right:* Moonset (detail) Holy Ghost Church.

Top left: Moonset Diamond Head Lighthouse, Oʻahu. *Top right:* Moonset, Hanalei Bay Church, Kauaʻi. *Bottom left:* Moonset over cemetery near Koloa, Kauaʻi. *Bottom right:* Moonrise Liliʻuokalani Hawaiian Church, Oʻahu. *Right:* Moonset Aloha Tower, Oʻahu.

Left: Moonset Aloha Tower, Oʻahu. *Right:* Moonset with catamaran, Oʻahu.

Left: Moonset Diamond Head Lighthouse, Oʻahu. *Top:* Moonset, Honolulu Harbor, Oʻahu. *Bottom:* Torch ginger.

Top: Moonset over the Hanalei Bridge & River, Kaua'i. *Bottom:* Moonrise over Anahulu River Bridge on the Kamehameha Highway, Hale'iwa, O'ahu.

Sunset at the War Memorial Natatorium, Sans Souci Beach, Oʻahu. Built in 1927 in memory of those local young men who died in World War I.

Ho'ohanohano "to honor"

The full moon hovers in the sky as ghostly and as peaceful as the Arizona Memorial which lies above the sunken hull of the battleship. It is here that 1,102 men went down with their ship in the surprise attack on the U.S. Pacific Fleet on December 7, 1941, hurtling the United States into World War II.

Above: Moonset, Plumeria tree. *Left:* Memorial for the 21 children and 3 adults that were killed in 1946 April Fool's Day tsunami, Hawai'i.

Moonset, Arizona Memorial, Pearl Harbor, O'ahu.

Top left: October sunset from Royal Kapuāiwa coconut grove, Molakaʻi. *Top right:* February sunset from Koko Head, Oʻahu. *Bottom:* March sunset, Magic Island, Oʻahu. *Opposite:* May sunset, Wailea Beach, Maui with cloud-covered Lānaʻi in the distance.

He'e nalu "to ride on the surf"

There is nothing more synonymous with Hawai'i than surfing. In early Hawai'i only the ali'i "royalty" were allowed to surf. When King Kamehameha II abolished the kapu "sacred" system in 1819 and surfing was permitted to all, he had no idea how popular "wave sliding" would become.

Within one hundred years Duke Kahanamoku was an Olympic gold medalist in swimming and a surfing hero on the beach of Waikīkī. Hawai'i's legendary surfing spots at Waimea, Sunset Beach, Pipeline, Mākaha, Jaws, and Hanalei Bay known for their 20 to 30 foot waves are mecca to most surfers around the world.

Opposite: Sunset with surfers on Old Man's Surf, O'ahu. *Above:* Sunrise on big waves at Waimea Bay, O'ahu.

"But tomorrow, ah tomorrow, I shall be out in that wonderful water, and I shall come in standing up…And if I fail tomorrow, I shall do it the next day, or the next."

JACK LONDON (1907)

Opposite: Sunrise with north shore surfer, Oʻahu. *Opposite right:* Moonset from Tunnels Beach toward Makana Cliff, Kauaʻi. *Above:* Sunset with big wave surfer, Turtle Bay, north shore Oʻahu. *Right:* Moonset from Waimea Bay, Oʻahu.

Moonset, Duke Kahanamoku Memorial on Waikīkī Beach, O'ahu. Kahahanamoku, 6'2" tall and weighing 183 lbs., first competed in the Olympics as a swimmer and won his first gold medals for the United States in 1911 at age 22. He continued to compete until he was 42, a span of 21 years which is a record that still stands.

Top left: Moonset, Natatorium, Sans Souci Beach, Oʻahu. *Top right:* Sunset, Diamond Head lighthouse, Oʻahu. *Bottom right:* Sunset, Hula dancers, Waikīkī Beach, Oʻahu. *Below:* Gold tree, Prima vera.

Left: Moon setting over a quiet surf at Duke Kahanamoku Memorial, Waikīkī Beach, Oʻahu. *Above:* Moonrise, Haleʻiwa Beach Park, Oʻahu. *Opposite:* Easter sunrise at Waipiʻo Valley, Hawaiʻi, where Kamehameha the Great grew up and learned the Hawaiian ways.

Opposite: Sunset with surfer at Kuʻemanu Heiau, altar for surfing, Keauhou-Kona, Hawaiʻi. *Left:* March sunset at Keauhou Beach, Hawaiʻi. *Right:* May sunset at Polihale "house of spirits" Beach, Kauaʻi.

"Impressed by the profound silence and repose that rested over the beautiful landscape, ... I gave voice to my thought. ...'What a picture is here slumbering in the solemn glory of the moon! How strong the rugged outlines of the dead volcano stand out against the clear sky! What a snowy fringe marks the bursting of the surf over the long, curved reef! How calmly the dim city sleeps yonder in the plain!'"

MARK TWAIN (1866)

Left: Moonrise Lēʻahi Crater (Diamond Head) from Kapiʻolani Park, Oʻahu. *Above left:* Moonrise Diamond Head. *Above right:* Full rainbow Diamond Head.

Opposite and above: Moonrise from Magic Island toward Waikīkī, Ala Wai Yacht Harbor and Diamond Head, Oʻahu.

Left: Moonrise Hilton Lagoon, Waikīkī, O'ahu. *Right top:* Moonrise over Ala Wai Yacht Harbor, O'ahu. *Right bottom:* Moonset over water from Outrigger Canoe Club. *Opposite:* Moonrise from Sand Island looking across Honolulu Harbor, O'ahu.

Top left: January sunset, Sans Souci Beach, Oʻahu. *Bottom left:* March sunset at Kūhiō Beach, Waikīkī. *Right:* December sunset from Waikīkī Beach, Oʻahu. *Opposite:* Sunset from Waikīkī Beach, Oʻahu.

Opposite top: Moonset on Kūhiō Beach Park toward the Royal Hawaiian Hotel, Oʻahu. *Opposite bottom:* Moonset in Banyan Tree, Waikīkī Beach, Oʻahu. *Above:* Dawn moon peaking through the clouds above Waikīkī from Lēʻahi Hospital, Oʻahu.

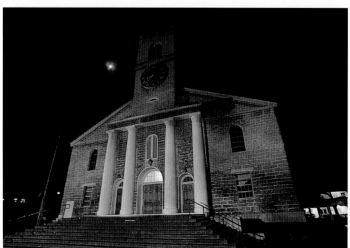 

Top left: Moonset Ali'iōlani Hale, State Judiciary Building with King Kamehameha statue. *Top right:* Moonrise above statue depicting the legend of Maui pulling up islands, Maui. *Bottom left:* Moonrise KawaiaHa'o Church. The "Westminster Abbey of Hawai'i," made of 14,000 blocks of coral. *Bottom right:* Moonrise at the Convention Center, O'ahu.

Top left: Moonrise behind the Waikīkī Business Plaza Building, Oʻahu. *Bottom left:* Moonset at the Duke Kahanamoku Memorial on Waikīkī Beach. *Above right:* Moonrise Waikīkī nightscape.

Top left: Moonrise behind King Kamehameha Memorial at Christmas, Honolulu, Oʻahu. *Top right:* Moonrise over fountain at Kapiʻolani Park, Oʻahu. *Bottom left:* Moonrise on Mokulua Drive, Lanikai, Oʻahu. *Bottom right:* Moonrise behind the Bank of Hawaiʻi Building, Oʻahu.

Left: Moonrise at the corner of South King and Bishop, Oʻahu. *Middle:* Moonrise at the corner of South King and Bishop, Oʻahu. *Right:* Moonrise at Honolulu Hale at Christmas, Oʻahu.

Opposite: February sunrise, Mokoliʻi, Oʻahu. *Top:* March sunset, fallen tree Waialea Bay, Kohala Coast, Hawaiʻi. *Bottom left:* Sunrise from Nāwiliwili Harbor toward the Ninini Point Lighthouse, Kauaʻi. *Bottom right:* Amaryllis.

Sunrise from Lanikai Beach, outrigger canoe.

Sunset from the Hawai'i Yacht Club, with canoe racers.

Moonrise over Mānana, known as Rabbit Island, Oʻahu.

"*Somehow, the love of the islands, like the love of a woman, just happens. One cannot determine in advance to love a particular woman, nor can one so determine to love Hawai'i. One sees, and one loves or does not love. With Hawai'i it seems always to be love at first sight.*"

JACK LONDON (1907)

Top: Sunset, peacock Mt. Olomana. *Right:* Sunset from Hanalei Pier toward Makahoa Point, Kaua'i. *Opposite:* February moonrise over Mokulua Islands from Lanikai Beach.